Asperger syndrome – an overview

Stephan Ehlers and
Christopher Gillberg

Translated from Swedish by
Charles Olsen

'To thine own self be true, and it must follow, as
the night the day, thou canst not then be false to
any man.' William Shakespeare

Authors

Stephan Ehlers is Head of Child and
Adolescent Psychiatry at Queen
Silvia's Hospital for Children and
Adolescents, Gothenburg, Sweden.

Christopher Gillberg is Professor of
Child and Adolescent Psychiatry at the
University of Gothenburg, Sweden,
and Visiting Professor at the National
Centre for Autism Studies, University
of Strathclyde, Glasgow, UK.

The translator in his own words

Charles Olsen was finally diagnosed with Asperger syndrome aged 24 years, 7 months and 27 days, having survived years of increasingly severe depression.

Some of the more memorable highlights of his protracted nervous breakdown included: seeking extremely brief asylum in a private psychiatric hospital (he checked out faster than he checked in); knocking back countless exotic drug cocktails (at one stage he had to suffer the ignominy of having a large needle jabbed into his pale, hairy posterior on a regular basis); signing up for a course of electroconvulsive therapy (he threw a fit on learning that this shocking treatment took place at the ungodly hour of 7 am); reluctantly acquiring several lifetimes' worth of provisional psychiatric diagnoses (he nevertheless enjoyed the freedom this gave him to select his own diagnosis according to his mood on any given day – very much like choosing a hat to go out in, or one's lunchtime sarnie); and courageously battling an army of mental health professionals who succeeded in failing to detect his underlying autism spectrum disorder (better luck next time).

Following his Asperger diagnosis (there is nothing negative or psychologically harmful about being 'labelled', provided that the 'label' is correct), he was additionally diagnosed with comorbid Tourette syndrome and attention deficits.

Perhaps not surprisingly, one of his circumscribed special interests is raising awareness of Asperger syndrome among GPs, adult psychiatrists and clinical psychologists.

He would like to dedicate his translation to Piers Bolduc, a man with Asperger syndrome who was wrongly diagnosed as having schizophrenia, and who was held in Broadmoor Special Hospital for nine long years.

First published in the UK 2006 by
The National Autistic Society,
393 City Road, London EC1V 1NG
Tel: 020 7833 2299
Email: nas@nas.org.uk
Website: www.autism.org.uk

First published in Sweden 1994 by Riksföreningen
Autism, Stockholm, under the title *Aspergers
syndrom – en översikt.*

Some revisions and additions made in 2006

ISBN 1 899280 59 6

Designed by Cottier and Sidaway

Printed by Chromatec

Contents

Preface

This book is intended primarily for parents of children diagnosed with Asperger syndrome, but is also for the various professionals wanting a concise description of this disability. Despite differences between them, children and adolescents with Asperger syndrome have one thing in common. And that is that, from an early age, they have experienced huge problems within the different areas described in this book.

We have used the letter 'A' throughout to denote people with Asperger syndrome in general. Since most people with the condition are male, we have opted for the pronoun 'he' when referring to A.

To shed light on how problems for A and his family appear in everyday life, we have illustrated the text with brief case descriptions. Names and certain facts have been changed so that individuals cannot be identified.

Introduction

Knowledge of children's mental
development has become ever greater in
recent decades. As our understanding of
what can be expected of children at
different stages of maturation increases,
we are able to tell more easily whether a
child is keeping pace with his age group,
or is in some way lagging behind or
exhibiting abnormal development.
We have also gained a better idea of
how difficulties within different areas
occur together.

The fact that we come across the same
combination of problems enables us to
speak of syndromes of various kinds.
The term 'syndrome' refers to a group of
symptoms which occur simultaneously
and form an identifiable condition. Our
knowledge of syndromes is based on
experience and, in many cases, has its
origin in observant doctors' descriptions
of previously unknown constellations
of problems.

Asperger syndrome has become a
generally accepted term for a condition
affecting people of normal or high
intelligence who have major difficulties
in social interaction, along with formal
speech, rigid body language,
idiosyncratic interests and clumsy
motor skills.

History and background

In 1944, the Austrian paediatrician, Hans Asperger, published an account of children with a particular combination of behaviour and social interaction problems.

Ten years later, and unaware of Asperger's paper, two American researchers described some boys with similar difficulties. They particularly emphasised that these children had very special interests. Further reports over the years have shown that children with this condition seem to exist throughout the world and are affected for life.

The English child psychiatrist, Lorna Wing, has been instrumental in increasing psychiatric knowledge of this frequently misunderstood group of children and adolescents. In 1981, Wing wrote a paper presenting Asperger's work, making it known to the English-speaking world. In the same paper she also described several cases from her own practice.

Many of the parents she met had suffered for years from being unable to obtain a name for their child's difficulties, and believed they were alone in their problems. Child psychiatrists they had encountered over the years had hesitated over making a definitive pronouncement, as the closest matching diagnosis was infantile autism.

Despite certain similarities, the children were not thought to belong within this diagnostic category. In order to distinguish this group from those with autism, Wing proposed the term 'Asperger's syndrome'.

Prevalence

In 1993, we (Ehlers and Gillberg) carried out a population-based study in Gothenburg, Sweden. This showed that between 0.4 and 0.7% of all children aged 7–16 years had problems and characteristics typical of Asperger syndrome.

Four times more boys than girls were found to have the condition, but the gap was less if we also included suspected cases. Earlier estimates, based on patients with Asperger syndrome, have indicated a far bigger gender difference.

The results show that Asperger syndrome is a relatively common disability which affects males more often than females. The difference between the sexes, however, does not appear to be as great as was previously thought.

Description of symptoms

Limited capacity for social interaction

According to most parents of children with Asperger syndrome, the first years of life are problem-free. The children are contented, obedient and easy to manage. However, some parents may have misgivings about their child's indifference to, or lack of interest in, other family members. Certain children, on the other hand, are described as overactive and restless, and their parents are particularly worried that they cannot differentiate between strangers and people whom they know well.

During his pre-school years, it usually becomes increasingly obvious to those around him that A's social development is abnormal. Curiosity about other people, so characteristic of this age, and the strong need to seek the company of peers is minimal; otherwise interaction occurs completely on the child's terms.

In the most typical case, A is already a precocious person by four years of age, who prefers to occupy himself on his own rather than play with the children at nursery school or in the neighbourhood. His formal, aloof demeanour is quite unlike that of the other children, who react with surprise and amazement. However, in the majority of cases, A gets on well with adults, who are able to appreciate his conversational or lecturing style. Some of the children in this group will seek the company of other children, but do not participate in any games as they prefer to be onlookers. Others have no respect for personal space when interacting and treat playmates more like objects than human beings. If his companions tire of allowing themselves to be controlled, or if they protest or walk off, A is unsympathetic and more inclined to become irritated and angry than upset.

Andrew isolated himself from his playmates and made contact with them in an odd way which resulted in him being bullied. The few times he played with other children were completely on his terms. On such occasions, Andrew would appoint himself leader and invent games with complicated rules that the other children had to follow. If they did not do as he said, he would become unreasonably angry.

A's inability to understand and adapt to other people stands out more and more as a social handicap during the pre-school years. In cases where he has not had the opportunity to meet other children to any great extent, and has been obliged to resort to adults, recognition of his difficulties may be delayed until the start of junior school.

It can be said that two different types of social interaction difficulties occur in children with Asperger syndrome. As should already be evident, some are passive and socially withdrawn, and have limited interaction with a few well-known adults.

Others, meanwhile, are active, markedly insensitive and disinhibited in relation to other people. This latter group has, as a rule, associated problems in the form of hyperactivity, impulsivity and inattention. Such problems are often referred to as attention-deficit/hyperactivity disorder (ADHD).

Throughout the Nordic countries, the concept of DAMP, which stands for deficits in attention, motor control and perception, has gained widespread acceptance over the past two decades. DAMP is a subgroup of ADHD, comprising ADHD symptoms in combination with clumsiness or so-called developmental coordination disorder. Sometimes ADHD/DAMP difficulties can predominate in childhood, to be overshadowed by social interaction problems in adolescence.

At school the biggest problem is generally at break time when A is thrown upon his own resources and forced to mix with fellow pupils in the playground. He will often go for a walk by himself following a regular route, try to remain indoors in the library, or look for a member of staff to be with. Some children with Asperger syndrome make easy targets for bullies on account of their unusual behaviour, particularly if they – like Andrew – easily lose control and have severe outbursts of anger.

People with Asperger syndrome have a distinct lack of social insight and common sense. For example, they are capable of making acutely accurate observations about particular aspects of other people's appearance straight out, regardless of the context. A seems unable to empathise with how the other person perceives what he has said, and does not appreciate the awkwardness of the situation. He appears more concerned with the accuracy of his statement than with the emotional reactions of the person singled out. In some cases, this tactlessness is coupled with a hypersensitivity to criticism directed towards him – A has a suspicious attitude and takes comments and remarks to heart for no reason.

Difficulty in understanding things and events in their social context generally becomes apparent from pre-school age onwards. Parents increasingly realise that it is not a question of their young child making naively sincere comments, but of an inability to understand and use implied rules of social interaction.

To some extent, many people with Asperger syndrome become aware in their teens of their limited ability to comprehend others. Typically, A will feel unsure of whether he has said the right thing, talked for just the right length of time, or given the other person a sufficient chance to speak etc.

Some people with Asperger syndrome avoid socialising. Others try to compensate by learning to use certain stock phrases, e.g. 'Just say if I'm talking too much', or by memorising how they should behave in different situations. As a result A may find it easier conversing with other people, but will appear gauche and socially rigid due to his learnt behaviour.

Reality, of course, is seldom totally the same from one time to the next. Despite some disadvantages, this method of consciously building up an 'inner encyclopaedia' of rules of conduct seems the best way of compensating for a lack of social intuition.

Lorna Wing mentions in her case histories a typical example of a young man who asked for a list of rules on how to meet and chat to girls. Whatever is done, however, difficulties will remain to a greater or lesser degree.

Ben, aged 20 years, wanted to date a girl the same age as him, but was unsure how he should go about this. He became interested in a woman who worked at the restaurant where he ate lunch. Ben came to the conclusion that it would be easiest to hand her a letter telling her about himself, mentioning that he wanted to go out with her. When she did not reply, he 'put her against the wall' and irritably asked why he had not heard from her. She then informed him that she was married with children, and that she had been extremely surprised and uneasy about his completely unexpected approach – something which had not occurred to Ben whatsoever. This example demonstrates the considerable difficulties that people with Asperger syndrome have in understanding the consequences of their actions.

Circumscribed special interests

One of the most striking features of children with Asperger syndrome is their special, often very circumscribed, interests.

In the typical case, A will impress those around him as early as pre-/primary school age with his huge factual knowledge within one or two narrow areas of interest. Examples include dinosaurs, military history, geography, languages, music, meteorology, computers, astronomy, the history of a royal family, steam engines or pure encyclopaedic knowledge of some kind, e.g. the top 20 best-selling singles of 1974, the 50 highest mountains etc. The list is endless and can in fact cover any area at all.

Although the areas of interest vary from child to child, there are some common characteristics. Generally speaking, A will not share his interest with a friend or with anyone in his family. Parents are often astonished at what their child has become interested in, and are sometimes seriously worried if he has too idiosyncratic an interest, e.g. poison formulae or gunpowder prescriptions.

A's knowledge is based on a vast amount of facts which are learnt by heart. Many of the children have a photographic memory and easily memorise large numbers of pages.

However, A's area of interest is very narrow and he shows clear indifference towards related fields of knowledge. His ability to explain meaning and context is remarkably poor, and he has no interest in making use of his knowledge in a more meaningful way. In many cases, A has an almost obsessive need to devote himself to his interest, which would consume every waking hour had he the power to decide. As a rule, everyone around him is forced to listen to the same extensive comments over and over again. Despite broad hints from the listener wanting to comment on or end the conversation, the child will continue his detailed monologue until the person may demonstratively walk off.

Chris taught himself to read single-handed when he was five years old. If there was something he really liked, he would learn long texts by heart. Dinosaurs became his major interest at a young age. Chris began to draw them and soon became a master of this art. It turned out that he had a photographic memory – he only had to look at a picture for a minute or so to be able to copy it exactly. The dinosaurs' Latin names were learnt just as easily. On a visit to an amusement park, Chris became delighted at the sight of some model dinosaurs. He quickly discovered that one of their names was misspelt, which made him most indignant.

Throughout the school years, the child's special ability to learn facts can have both advantages and disadvantages. A pronounced mathematical or linguistic talent impresses classmates and **A** may become known as 'The Professor'. Pure encyclopaedic knowledge of some kind, e.g. bus routes, is not appreciated in the same way and **A** will often be ridiculed and bullied. Some of the children comment on and correct others in class (including the teacher) over factual errors, spelling mistakes etc. and are disliked because of their 'I know best' attitude.

Our experience of girls with Asperger syndrome indicates that they are just as preoccupied with their special interests, though these are based on rote knowledge to a lesser extent.

Danielle gradually developed an interest in paper bags, which she collected with such zeal that her parents became extremely concerned. Her interest was at its peak between eight and ten years of age, when it suddenly ceased and was replaced by an almost fanatical commitment against animal experiments. She would write long letters to various authorities but would not expect a reply. At the same time she owned a guinea pig, which she cared for rather irresponsibly. The animal died whilst the family were on holiday, presumably because it had been left unattended for several days.

The pattern of interests generally persists throughout life. This does not necessarily mean that **A** will stick to the same area of interest, but rather that his specific interests will usually change over the years. Some adults join clubs where they can socialise with others around a common interest.

In some instances, the special interest leads to a career. Parents and the treatment team must decide in the individual case whether A's interest or fixation is the kind one should try to curb through strict rules, e.g. fire-setting, or instead the kind one should enable him to practise at the expense of social interaction, e.g. a musical talent.

In the vast majority of cases, however, it is a matter of helping A to acquire more appropriate social behaviours and encouraging him to mix with peers. As he becomes more socially competent, the intensity with which he pursues his interest normally lessens or assumes more acceptable forms.

Compulsive behaviour and insistence on routines

People with Asperger syndrome usually develop a need for routines early on. For example, A will typically demand his own set place at the dining table or in the car, and will become irritated or angry if those around him do not adapt.

Some children with Asperger syndrome have special rituals associated with everyday activities such as brushing teeth or going to bed. Parents initially view this as a passing phase, but, unlike the behaviour of typically developing children, the need for routines tends to increase over the years.

Many teenagers and adults with Asperger syndrome have mapped out their whole lives according to a particular pattern, which makes them extremely limited and vulnerable. A seemingly trivial change to their daily routine creates so much confusion in their world of ideas that nothing gets done.

Compulsive repetition of certain actions or thoughts is also common, e.g. routinely counting everyone on entering a room. A does not consider his need for a rigid or pedantic order strange, despite the reactions of other people.

During their teens, some of the children become aware of their particular idiosyncrasies. At the same time A is unable to suppress his strong need to carry out certain actions, and will try to conceal his compulsiveness by performing these rituals in secret.

Others with Asperger syndrome have no insight into their own difficulties and continue to force those around them to adapt in accordance with them. In many cases, compulsive behaviour contributes to A isolating himself socially.

A remarkable number of children and adolescents in this group have major problems with food and eating. Only a few dishes will be eaten by them. Parents speak despairingly of the constant battle at the dining table and how they eventually had to give in and serve the same meals day in, day out.

Emma, a 20-year-old woman, had read that it was healthy to eat regularly and often – ideally every four hours. She therefore began to adopt this practice. Because the book did not mention that this only applied to the daytime, she set her alarm to ring every four hours during the night in order to get up and eat. She disturbed the others in her group home so much that she had to move out. Later on, she was persuaded to alter her mealtime ritual to the extent that she only got up once a night to eat.

Another problem that tends to increase over the years, and which contrasts with the need for routines, concerns A's ability to cope with simple everyday tasks and attend to personal hygiene. A frequently has no idea at all how often he should shower or change his clothes. He also lacks a sense of fashion. Parents gradually learn to get him a few matching garments which he will learn to change at fixed intervals.

Freddie has tremendous difficulty in getting going in the morning and setting off for school. He will only get dressed if told what to do, e.g. put on trousers, socks etc. His parents are forced to tell him absolutely everything so that he does this. It is completely impossible for Freddie to do several things at once. He cannot even chew and cut food for his next mouthful simultaneously.

Speech, language and communication problems

It is not uncommon for parents of a child with Asperger syndrome to report that his early speech development was delayed. It might have taken until two years of age, or perhaps even longer, before he started talking, but, in contrast, everything subsequently came 'all at once'. From 'nothing', **A** began speaking in full sentences of two and three words using a large and varied vocabulary. Other children in this group have completely normal speech development or even learn to talk earlier than is usual.

Irrespective of these differences, the children generally have no period of baby talk. As early as pre-school age, many speak in a typically precocious way with remarkable poise regarding their choice of words and sentence structure. Many become meticulously accurate in their use of language and will often use dictionaries assiduously in order to increase their vocabulary and learn 'exact' meanings.

A finds it disturbing that other people do not speak in a similarly correct fashion and will not hesitate to point this out. It may be that his need for a precise meaning is so strong that he has difficulty in understanding that words can have more than one definition. He will perhaps only accept the meaning that a word had the first time he heard it. His language may also contain features of invented words and expressions which cannot be suppressed in social settings.

George, ten years of age, firmly pointed out to his mum that she should not use the word 'kid' when talking about him, since it had a negative connotation. Instead she should say 'child', as this had a positive one. When his mother explained that she had said 'kid' affectionately, George became irritated and forbade her from using that term in the future.

A's formal linguistic self-confidence stands in sharp contrast with his ability to use language in social contexts. It is often vitally important to catch the differences in a word's meaning depending on when and how it is said.

If spoken messages are interpreted as isolated comments with no connection to the situation, this gives rise to various problems, e.g. difficulties in grasping ironic remarks and in understanding puns, idioms and metaphors.

A quite simply misses the abstract and ambiguous content of language and instead interprets words literally; an idiomatic phrase such as 'to spend a penny' is construed as a monetary transaction, while the metaphor 'at daggers drawn' has a concrete meaning. A is likely to answer yes to the question 'Can you shut the window?' without making any attempt to carry out the request.

In conversation, a spoken message will, furthermore, often have an underlying aim which can be just as important as its actual verbal content. One has to understand the reason why someone says something. Above all, it is a person's prosody – i.e. the volume, pitch, stress, rhythm and rate of their speech – as well as their facial expressions, eye contact and gestures that signal a message's purpose and convey values and emotions.

A distinctive feature of people with Asperger syndrome is their limited means of communicating through intonation, eye contact, facial expressions and gestures. As a rule, A shows particular abnormalities of prosody and his speech is often monotonous or spasmodic. His voice can be exceptionally shrill and at an inappropriate volume – he will either speak too loudly or too quietly.

A's gaze is considered abnormal and usually described as stiff, staring or piercing. He displays a lack of give-and-take in his use of eye contact and his face is often blank or confined to a few expressions.

In general, A's repertoire of gestures is also extremely limited. Some individuals with Asperger syndrome have formal, old-fashioned body language. Difficulty in reading other people's body language contributes to unspoken aims, intentions and emotional aspects being missed.

These types of linguistic problems are usually termed 'semantic-pragmatic'. Semantic relates to the different meanings that words have, while pragmatic to how words are used when interacting with other people. It is thus partly to do with difficulties in understanding the varying meanings words have depending on the situation, and partly to do with difficulties in putting a spoken message into its social and emotional context: i.e. difficulties in 'reading between the lines'.

These semantic-pragmatic problems undoubtedly stem from the obvious difficulties that people with Asperger syndrome have in empathising with other people's thoughts, feelings and opinions. Empathy problems have a profoundly restricting effect on genuine social communication.

> Henry is a 25-year-old man who loves to deliver long monologues on his favourite interests. Despite there being only two of us in the room, Henry talks at a volume more suitable for a gathering of 15 people. Henry realises that he has tremendous difficulty in sensing an atmosphere. He has learnt not to try to crack a joke or fool around by saying something amusing, as this has resulted in embarrassing situations quite a few times.

Motor clumsiness

Most people with Asperger syndrome have generally been regarded as slow and clumsy with awkward, ill-coordinated movements from a very early age. As a rule, their pattern of gait is rigid and stilted. This motor stiffness may strengthen one's impression of A being a precocious person.

Some of the children distinguish themselves by their particular mannerisms with exaggerated, slightly old-fashioned or formal gestures. A predominant interest in sport, common to most boys, is usually absent. In the typical case, A is clearly uninterested in doing sport of any kind. Both his ball skills and his grasp of team games are impaired. Classmates do not feel that A merits a place in the team when playing sport in PE.

> Ian, who was in middle school, refused to take part in rounders. His awkward way of moving was not suited to team sports. Instead, he gave a detailed lecture in class on cricket.

Our experience of adults with Asperger syndrome tells us that the majority are extremely impractical people who are 'all fingers and thumbs'. Generally speaking, A will not get any further than the instructions when doing IKEA-type DIY jobs. The practical accomplishment of such tasks is too complicated or takes forever.

John is a 26-year-old Swedish man who is fluent in English and German. Among other things, he speaks three different German dialects and has an exceptionally broad knowledge of geography and economic statistics.

However, he is incapable of running his own home and has board and lodging with a female relation who is over 80 years old. John spoke of his dream to be so rich that he would be spared all practical chores. For example, he had worked out that he would then be able to throw away his socks after one wear, and hence would not have to worry about his laundry or be dependent on his relative.

Intelligence and specific learning difficulties

The aforementioned population-based study carried out in Gothenburg showed that the intelligence of the children with Asperger syndrome fell within the normal range. The proportion who were of high intelligence and low average intelligence respectively was roughly equal. Other studies have shown that even the occasional child with mild learning disability can have problems typical of Asperger syndrome.

A characteristic of people with Asperger syndrome is that, regardless of certain variations in their general intellectual level, they demonstrate a particular pattern on psychological testing.

As a rule, they do best at the subtests which measure verbal ability, e.g. 'Vocabulary', 'Information' and 'Similarities'. The results of the subtests which measure perceptual ability, i.e. the comprehension of shapes and patterns, are usually lower.

Highly typical is their difficulty in solving tasks that presuppose an ability to imagine and empathise with other people's thoughts and feelings. Furthermore, their ability to perform several kinds of tasks simultaneously and come up with suitable strategies to problems by trial and error is greatly limited.

This unevenness in the test profile explains why children with Asperger syndrome, despite having seemingly excellent intellectual capacities, often fail at school and are later unable to cope with the demands of daily adult life.

> Karl could already read by four years of age. On starting junior school, it was noted that he was ahead of his peers intellectually, particularly in maths where he had a special talent for multiplying large sums in his head. Towards the end of middle school, his teacher considered that his intellectual abilities had declined and, if anything, he was trailing his classmates.

As the demands to seek knowledge more independently increase, and as the understanding of what is learnt becomes more important than rote memory skills, A – like the example of Karl – will often have problems keeping up.

21

Many parents of children with Asperger syndrome have spoken of how their child's difficulties at school came as a surprise. They never expected that someone who could already read in nursery school, with a large vocabulary and a greater factual knowledge than anyone else in class (including the teacher), would have any specific learning difficulties.

During the course of junior and middle school, it becomes more apparent that children with Asperger syndrome have particular problems. For instance, they need specific help and instruction in order to start and complete schoolwork. They also require much longer than the majority of their classmates and perform considerably worse when working under time pressure.

Good rote memory skills on their own are no longer enough. Children with Asperger syndrome have to solve tasks in a certain order to avoid getting muddled and need far longer than most other pupils in their class, as they work extremely carefully and circumstantially with every exercise.

A lacks flexibility when solving problems of various kinds and has difficulty in rethinking and finding a new strategy if his first course of action does not work.

Associated problems

The link between Asperger syndrome and motor clumsiness is something which even Hans Asperger commented on. Clumsiness generally has a very early onset and is not affected significantly by training.

Besides motor difficulties, many children with Asperger syndrome have additional problems in the form of hyperactivity, impulsivity and inattention (so-called ADHD or DAMP). Differentiating between severe DAMP and Asperger syndrome is difficult in certain cases.

In reality, there is no clear dividing line between the two. A child may fit the diagnosis of DAMP at one age, while at another age the diagnosis of Asperger syndrome will better account for his problems.

Some children with Asperger syndrome have tics and the risk of these further increases if they also suffer from DAMP problems. A tic is an involuntary, sudden and rapid muscle contraction of the face or body.

In more severe cases, the child develops particular patterns of movement such as crouching down, spinning round and so on. Tics can also be vocal. Here the child expresses different sounds involuntarily, e.g. throat-clearing, coughing, uttering words or whole sentences.

If both motor and vocal tics have been present for more than one year, Tourette syndrome is normally diagnosed. Should severe tics occur as an additional handicap, an element of compulsion of various kinds can be expected also to be present in many instances. However, it is important to point out that Asperger syndrome in itself entails a compulsive attitude towards the environment in most cases.

Within psychiatry, compulsions are usually evaluated on the basis of whether or not the affected individual recognises that his compulsive needs are senseless. His ability to resist performing them is also taken into account.

From this perspective, it is evident that the vast majority of people with Asperger syndrome differ from those with so-called obsessive-compulsive disorder in that they themselves do not suffer from their compulsions or consider them odd and disturbing. A will not actually seek help to be free of them. In many cases, making such a differentiation in respect of children is difficult. With adolescents and adults this is usually more obvious if the individual himself or those around him suffer (predominantly) from his pedantry and compulsive behaviour.

In this context, it is interesting that the diagnosis of obsessive-compulsive personality disorder (OCPD) is used within adult psychiatry. If one thinks about it, this diagnosis very aptly describes the compulsive sides particularly of teenagers and adults with Asperger syndrome (see Appendix). This shows that such problems have been noticed in the past, albeit from a different angle – the compulsive behaviour has been emphasised more than the social handicap.

It is undoubtedly the case that many people with a diagnosis of OCPD have problems typical of Asperger syndrome. The same is also true of some other conditions within adult psychiatry: in particular, type II schizophrenia, 'simple schizophrenia' and several of the many personality disorders (e.g. borderline, paranoid, schizoid, schizotypal).

In her research into anorexia nervosa, Maria Råstam has demonstrated that certain girls who are markedly obsessive also meet criteria for Asperger syndrome. The few boys with anorexia nervosa who have been investigated have had associated 'Asperger problems' to an even greater degree.

The boundaries with autism

It is clear that Asperger syndrome shares strong similarities with autism. Lorna Wing, who coined the term 'Asperger's syndrome', even thinks that Leo Kanner, the American child psychiatrist who first described infantile autism, and Hans Asperger actually wrote about children with the same kinds of impairments.

In a large-scale 1979 study, Wing and a colleague found that, if a child had social interaction difficulties, he would also have behaviour and communication problems. These were deemed to reflect limited social imagination.

Wing is of the opinion that Asperger syndrome and autism are such similar conditions that they can be seen as two branches of the same tree. To put it another way, autism and Asperger syndrome are part of a spectrum, with the common denominator being difficulties within the following areas ('Wing's triad'):

1. inability to interact socially, particularly with age peers;
2. impaired verbal and non-verbal communication;
3. limited inner imaginary world, replaced by repetitive activities and/or one-sided interests.

In addition, Wing considers that the children described by both Kanner and Asperger exhibited their most typical abnormalities within these three areas, though they varied in severity. Her study also showed that even some children with severe learning disability displayed difficulties within these areas.

Christopher and Carina Gillberg have elaborated this viewpoint and divided the children into groups according to the extent of their difficulties, which seems to be strongly linked to their general intellectual level (Fig.1).

Children of normal intelligence with Asperger syndrome comprise the upper field, Kanner's group with infantile autism and mild–moderate learning disability comprise the middle field, while children with severe learning disability comprise the lower field.

Concentrating solely on the Kanner and Asperger groups, one finds a wide individual variation and that the children develop within their ranges of ability in line with their age. People who have had typical Kanner autism in childhood may fit Asperger's description better as teenagers.

Although there is consensus on this viewpoint, there is still uncertainty as to whether Asperger syndrome should be regarded as synonymous with autism in children of normal or high intelligence, or instead as an independent subgroup within an autism spectrum.

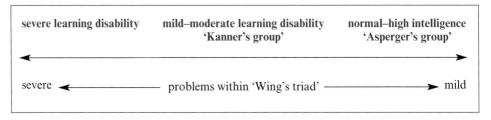

Fig.1. Asperger syndrome as a subgroup of an autism spectrum. Adapted from Gillberg and Gillberg (1989).

Diagnostic criteria

In recent years, diagnostic criteria
for Asperger syndrome have been
compiled, partly to facilitate
diagnosis and partly to create a
uniform view of the condition.
The criteria should also be seen
as a means of promoting research.

Three different proposals for
diagnostic criteria are set out in Table
1. Despite having much in common, it
is clear nevertheless that the various
sets of criteria vary from one another
in their emphasis of different aspects
of the disability.

In 1994, further suggested criteria
were published (DSM-IV), which do
not differ in principle from those put
forward by the World Health
Organization (see Table 1.3).
Ongoing and future research will
provide us with better opportunities
for differentiating the difficulties
that are most characteristic of
Asperger syndrome.

1.1	Gillberg and Gillberg (1989), Gillberg (1991)
1	**Social impairment (extreme egocentricity)** **(at least two of the following):** (a) difficulties interacting with peers (b) indifference to peer interactions (c) difficulties interpreting social cues (d) socially and emotionally inappropriate behaviour.
2	**Narrow interest (at least one of the following):** (a) exclusion of other activities (b) repetitive adherence (c) more rote than meaning.
3	**Compulsive need for introducing routines and interests** **(at least one of the following):** (a) which affect every aspect of the individual's everyday life (b) which affect others.
4	**Speech and language peculiarities** **(at least three of the following):** (a) delayed speech development (b) superficially perfect expressive language (c) formal, pedantic language (d) odd prosody, peculiar voice characteristics (e) impairment of comprehension, including misinterpretations of literal/implied meanings.

5	**Non-verbal communication problems (at least one of the following):** (a) limited use of gestures (b) clumsy/gauche body language (c) limited facial expressions (d) inappropriate facial expression (e) peculiar, stiff gaze.
6	**Motor clumsiness:** (a) poor performance in neurodevelopmental tests.

1.2	Szatmari et al. (1989)
1	**Solitary (at least two of the following):** (a) no close friends (b) avoids others (c) no interest in making friends (d) a loner.
2	**Impaired social interaction (at least one of the following):** (a) approaches others only to have own needs met (b) a clumsy social approach (c) one-sided responses to peers (d) difficulty sensing feelings of others (e) detached from feelings of others.
3	**Impaired non-verbal communication** **(at least one of the following):** (a) limited facial expression (b) unable to read emotion from facial expression of child (c) unable to give message with eyes (d) does not look at others (e) does not use hands to express oneself (f) gestures are large and clumsy (g) comes too close to others.
4	**Odd speech (at least two of the following):** (a) abnormalities in inflection (b) talks too much (c) talks too little (d) lack of cohesion to conversation (e) idiosyncratic use of words (f) repetitive patterns of speech.

1.3	ICD-10, World Health Organization (1993)
1	**There is no clinically significant general delay in spoken or receptive language or cognitive development.** (a) Diagnosis requires that single words should have developed by two years of age or earlier and that communicative phrases be used by three years of age or earlier. Self-help skills, adaptive behaviour, and curiosity about the environment during the first three years should be at a level consistent with normal intellectual development. However, motor milestones may be somewhat delayed and motor clumsiness is usual (although not a necessary diagnostic feature). Isolated special skills, often related to abnormal preoccupations, are common, but are not required for diagnosis.
2	**There are qualitative abnormalities in reciprocal social interaction in at least two of the following areas:** (a) failure adequately to use eye-to-eye gaze, facial expression, body posture, and gesture to regulate social interaction (b) failure to develop (in a manner appropriate to mental age, and despite ample opportunities) peer relationships that involve a mutual sharing of interests, activities, and emotions (c) lack of socio-emotional reciprocity as shown by an impaired or deviant response to other people's emotions; or lack of modulation of behaviour according to social context; or a weak integration of social, emotional, and communicative behaviours (d) lack of spontaneous seeking to share enjoyment, interests, or achievements with other people (e.g. a lack of showing, bringing, or pointing out to other people objects of interest to the individual).

3	The individual exhibits an unusually intense, circumscribed interest or restricted, repetitive, and stereotyped patterns of behaviour, interests, and activities in at least one of the following areas:
	(a) an encompassing preoccupation with one or more stereotyped and restricted patterns of interest that are abnormal in content or focus; or one or more interests that are abnormal in their intensity and circumscribed nature though not in their content or focus
	(b) apparently compulsive adherence to specific, non-functional routines or rituals
	(c) stereotyped and repetitive motor mannerisms that involve either hand or finger flapping or twisting, or complex whole body movements
	(d) preoccupations with part-objects or non-functional elements of play materials (such as their odour, the feel of their surface, or the noise or vibration that they generate).

Table 1. Diagnostic criteria for Asperger syndrome.

Other diagnostic criteria

The National Autistic Society's Centre for Social and Communication Disorders has developed its own diagnostic criteria, DISCO. For further details please contact:

The Centre for Social and
Communication Disorders
Elliot House
113 Masons Hill
Bromley
Kent BR2 9HT
Tel: 020 8466 0098
Fax: 020 8466 0118
Email: elliot.house@nas.org.uk

Causes

The cause of Asperger syndrome is not fully known, but genetic (inherited) factors seem to be important. Remarkably often, one of the parents will have similar difficulties, although not as pronounced. Furthermore, there will usually be other relatives who are described as eccentric, slightly odd and perhaps socially isolated people.

In recent years, several reports have indicated a genetic link between Asperger syndrome and autism due to the presence of both conditions within the same family of siblings. However, it has not been possible to identify a specific hereditary factor or mode of inheritance.

There is general agreement among researchers that psychosocial factors or particular experiences in childhood do not cause disabilities such as Asperger syndrome. Instead, Asperger syndrome should be regarded as a form of developmental disorder/condition affecting several important functions of the child's communication and interaction with the environment.

An English researcher, Digby Tantam, has compared Asperger syndrome to colour-blindness. He suggests that colour-blindness may be an unrecognised disability for which most people have no word. Society notices how the colour-blind person's behaviour makes him stand out: through his odd colour combination of clothes, the badly adjusted colour balance on his television, his lack of certain colours when describing objects etc.

If we continue with this analogy and attempt to identify the cause of his various problems, it proves more difficult than one would imagine. The disability can vary in severity from person to person. In addition, some colour-blind individuals have learnt to compensate for their handicap by, for example, observing changes in the brightness of traffic lights rather than changes in their colour.

Likewise, we can try to envisage what problems arise for someone with a 'social colour-blindness' such as Asperger syndrome and how he can learn to compensate for his disability in different ways.

Investigation

Basic investigation has two main aims if a child is suspected of having Asperger syndrome. The first is to ascertain whether the various symptoms and difficulties are typical of Asperger syndrome and to evaluate the child's developmental level and intelligence profile.

This part of the investigation comprises a thorough medical history, a physical examination and tests conducted by a psychologist. If a specific language appraisal is necessary, a speech therapist will also be consulted.

The investigation's other main aim is to try to establish why the child has Asperger syndrome. As stated above, in many cases, the family history indicates that genetic factors play an important role, either as an isolated phenomenon, or in combination with other factors such as a difficult birth resulting in a lack of oxygen for the baby.

We recommend that parents have a chromosome analysis done on their child by means of a simple blood test. In this way, we can either confirm or rule out certain changes in his genetic make-up, e.g. the fragile X chromosome which can be associated with Asperger syndrome.

Other examinations include electroencephalogram (EEG), which measures brain cells' electrical discharges, and auditory brainstem response (ABR), which assesses the functioning of the part of the brain that, amongst other things, regulates wakefulness. Neither causes the child discomfort and both usually take less than an hour to carry out. Further tests may be appropriate in the event of certain specific problems or issues.

Outcome

Hans Asperger investigated some 200 children with such problems over many years and concluded that the condition must be regarded as a lifelong disability. He considered the various difficulties a mark of a particular personality disorder which did not just have negative aspects but positive ones also.

He consequently reflected on some of the children's special intellectual abilities – being able to devote all their time to a very narrow area of interest and to develop their own train of thought unswervingly – and came to believe that these could result in original, ground-breaking thinking within, for example, maths and physics.

Among other cases, he described that of a boy who showed an exceptional mathematical talent at a very early age. The boy was completely absorbed in maths and, as a young adult, wrote a thesis on one of Newton's equations in which he had found an error. Throughout his life, he was extremely inept socially and dependent on extensive help and support.

However, Asperger also described children whose activities were confined to stereotyped repetition and other pointless interests and explained that this was due to lower IQ. He speculated on the combination of dry logical thought, emotional coldness and social isolation, and wondered whether this was an extreme manifestation of 'male intelligence'.

Hans Asperger believed the prognosis to be relatively good in spite of the prominent social handicap. This may have been due in some part to him concentrating his case descriptions on the most able children and how they fared career-wise.

Follow-up in recent years of children with Asperger syndrome does not paint as positive a picture, specifically regarding social and psychological adjustment. Marriage and stable couple relationships do occur but, more often than not, the individual continues to live at home with his parents or, as in John's case, with a relation. After one or two unsuccessful attempts at finding a partner, A will often withdraw and choose instead to socialise in a conventional way with a few relatives or 'close' friends. Club activities revolving around the special interest can, to some extent, replace a traditional family life.

Our knowledge is limited in this area but some known cases indicate that, remarkably often, it is the maternal type of woman who takes charge who can cope best with living together with a man with Asperger syndrome. A sympathetic attitude and excellent social adaptation are the qualities which the partner will most likely require for a relationship with a gauche and egocentric person to be possible.

From adolescence onwards, psychiatric problems in the form of depression, anxiety, and crisis and stress reactions are not particularly uncommon. Feelings of being watched or followed may also occur.

Follow-up by Lorna Wing reveals a slightly higher suicide rate among young adults with Asperger syndrome compared with the general population. The majority of these problems undoubtedly stem from the painful experience of being different or inadequate and having little prospect of being able to do anything about this.

Lisa is someone who is unable to withstand too much stress or too many changes in her everyday life. As a child she was a definite loner. Lisa could not understand her parents' concern over her self-imposed isolation, but was happy to devote herself to her schoolwork and special interests.

In her teens Lisa began to ponder over why she was different. She also became anxious that she could not keep up sufficiently at school. During a stressful spell in Year 10, Lisa became severely confused and developed persecution mania. She only recovered after several months' care and treatment with medication. The following year she fell ill again. This episode also necessitated a lengthy period of drug therapy.

Lisa has been well since then but is a sensitive person with typical features of Asperger syndrome.

Modern working life makes great demands on flexibility and social skills. Not even within the academic world is there a haven nowadays for the eccentric, bookish 'professor' or unworldly narrow specialist. Limited social competence combined with major difficulties in juggling several things at once make a person with Asperger syndrome highly vulnerable within most occupations.

In cases where the special interest has led to a career, and where A has been accepted despite his odd personality, there is a chance of him settling and being successful within his field. Most people with Asperger syndrome, however, are best suited to jobs with clearly-defined tasks without time pressure.

The National Autistic Society (NAS) has developed a number of supported employment schemes across the UK for adults with Asperger syndrome. For further information please see the NAS contact details on the back cover.

Michael is a 22-year-old man who, via a government training scheme, was given the chance to try out various routine jobs. He felt at home in an office where he got to do filing by himself.

Michael willingly spoke in detail about the five different types of tasks which he would perform to a T every day. His marked inflexibility and obsessiveness restricted him, and he became clearly disturbed if he could not work to his own schedule.

A small minority of individuals with Asperger syndrome commit serious and bizarre acts to varying degrees.

Nick, a tall young man with Asperger syndrome, has been fixated on fire since childhood. During a very stressful period in adolescence, he set light to a neighbour's house. Luckily it was empty and nobody was hurt.

Photography is also a hobby of his. Unfortunately he is obsessively interested in taking pictures of young girls on the beach and, furthermore, will usually go up to them afterwards and hug them – something which has led to several unpleasant incidents.

Oliver, another young man with Asperger syndrome, was politically active (an 'anti-imperialist') and, together with a friend, carried out an attack on an 'American' hamburger restaurant. He threw a firebomb through the window after closing time, so that no one would come to any harm. However, it had never occurred to him that the restaurant was situated in a building containing flats.

Common to Nick and Oliver is their inability to see their behaviour in a broader context. They thought and acted in a single-minded and/or obsessive manner based on their own particular interests or beliefs.

During police questioning they came across as being naïve and frank. Their attitude following their respective incidents was characterised principally by the phrase 'I didn't think of that'. Neither of the young men had realised the consequences of their actions. It was also typical that they did not try to shirk responsibility for what had happened but honestly recounted what they had done.

In both cases their disability was taken into account and their sentence adjusted accordingly.

The following case description shows that, with a correct diagnosis in childhood, focus on strengths rather than just on difficulties, and the continued regular support of an autism expert, the outcome in people with Asperger syndrome can be excellent.

Penny, at 32 years, was married to a successful artist. Together they had a three-year-old daughter who was developing normally and seemed a very bright, albeit slightly 'serious' girl. Penny herself had recently been awarded a scholarship to art school following a major exhibition of her paintings in a famous downtown gallery. She was rather tired and occasionally 'stressed out' but, by and large, her life was 'on track' and she considered herself 'a very lucky and happy person'.

Penny had been diagnosed with Asperger syndrome at age 11 years, at a time when she was very socially isolated and had had a succession of extremely bizarre and all-absorbing interests. Several members of her extended family had previously been diagnosed with autism or Asperger syndrome. She had been the subject of much bullying at school, and had failed most subjects in spite of having an overall IQ of 110.

At the time of diagnosis, she was observed to have excellent visual skills and an extremely well-developed talent for colours and for the blending of pigments. Until then, her teachers had tried to dissuade her from spending time on such 'useless things'.

After she was diagnosed, she was instead allowed extra time with an art teacher and had an autism-friendly structure applied to her curriculum in other subjects. She soon started exhibiting her art in the classroom and later in school competitions held in the main hallway.

The bullying soon stopped. She was fortunate to have the support of a psychiatrist with expertise in autism four to six times a year over the next ten years, until she met her future husband at the age of 22.

Guidelines for counselling, interventions and follow-up

An important starting point for all interventions is knowing that Asperger syndrome is a lifelong disability. An educational programme tailored to the individual child forms the basis for long-term rehabilitation work. However, the need for (and interest in) interventions varies. Some children with Asperger syndrome will be helped simply by investigation, diagnosis and the provision of information. Others will need the support of one or more skilled people over the course of many years. This calls for close collaboration between parents, school and the diagnostic team.

Secondary psychiatric problems such as depression, anxiety or milder confusional states are fairly common, particularly from adolescence onwards, and should be seen as a reaction to demands that A is unable to meet. One should also be on the lookout for various compulsive behaviours which often increase with age. Treatment with medication should be restricted and always complementary to other measures.

Many children and adolescents with Asperger syndrome are impractical and uninterested in learning to attend to personal hygiene and other important daily chores. From a young age they require continual training so as not to become too dependent on others as adults.

In short, it can be said that early diagnosis, accurate information for all concerned and appropriate interventions will go some way towards helping A overcome many of the difficulties which his disability entails. Moreover, if the environment adapts/is adapted to his limited ability within a variety of areas, there is a good chance of successful employment and a relatively independent adult life.

In other cases, sheltered work and housing may be the most realistic alternative. Both the person with Asperger syndrome and his family need support, advice and help of a social and practical nature over many years.

It can be important for the teenager to be able to meet regularly with an adult who has considerable experience of

Asperger syndrome, or perhaps with other adolescents with the same diagnosis, in order to discuss problems in his everyday life. We believe that a supportive educational contact such as this can prevent the fairly frequent episodes of depression in many teenagers and young adults with Asperger syndrome.

Supportive therapy

Psychologist Christina Lögdahl has been counselling older teenagers with Asperger syndrome on a regular basis for several years. In her experience, therapeutic work requires an intimate knowledge of the particular way of thinking of people with Asperger syndrome. As far as possible, the therapist must endeavour to think like A, while at the same time using their own judgement to guide him in the right direction.

It is important to start by discussing issues which A raises and not to steer the topic of conversation to too great an extent. If the therapist digresses too much, A will simply get confused. In addition, the therapist must gain A's trust and succeed in establishing a rapport. Finally, the therapist will need to have a lot of patience, as this is time-consuming work which can hardly be rushed.

The supportive therapy can be divided into various phases.

To begin with, A will talk almost exclusively about his interests. Here the therapist must listen patiently and not rush things, openly admitting their ignorance within A's special fields.

After a while, A will usually stop talking about his interests. He will have difficulty in finding words and will start speaking more slowly, perhaps asking the therapist to pose questions in order to discover the most relevant area to discuss. This phase is probably the most delicate. Confidence in the therapist is crucial in determining how meaningful the conversations are.

Gradually the next phase gets under way with A speaking unaided, enquiring about things which he does not understand. For example, these may be social situations he has been in, thoughts on the opposite sex, worries about illnesses, his own and other people's disabilities, verbal expressions and jokes.

The therapist's job is to explain matters raised by A in language that he can comprehend. Over a long period of time, extreme clarity is needed. Counter-questioning, albeit tactful, is necessary to ensure that A has grasped the essence of the conversation.

After yet more time, A can start talking about his experience of being different. Many individuals with Asperger syndrome have felt this way for as long as they can remember, but have lacked words to describe it. They are also often deeply hurt due to bad treatment from other people. Self-reflection and concern for others can increase markedly during this phase.

Counselling does not produce a cure, but will make social contexts more intelligible. Furthermore, it can improve social adaptation and help reduce the tendency to social isolation. From adolescence onwards, supportive therapy can be a suitable complement to other more practical educational interventions.

Recent educational research has shown that people with Asperger syndrome benefit greatly from writing down advice and experiences, which they can return to again and again. Knowledge sinks in completely differently when in written form and, by continuing to read and recite to themselves how they should go about things, learning becomes more effective.

Parent support groups

Within several regional branches of The National Autistic Society there are specific parent groups devoted to Asperger syndrome. Many parents regard contact with families in similar situations as a vital support and a valuable opportunity to exchange knowledge and experiences.

Summary

Asperger syndrome occurs in children of normal or high intelligence and is characterised by a particular combination of: (a) major difficulties in social interaction; (b) formal speech; (c) rigid body language; (d) idiosyncratic interests; and (e) clumsy motor skills.

Problems appear early on and affect the individual throughout life. It is estimated that at least 4 in every 1,000 children aged 7–16 years have Asperger syndrome. Far more boys are affected than girls.

The condition primarily entails a handicap interacting with other people, but also results in significant general adaptation problems, and an inability to cope with the demands of school, work and everyday life.

The boundaries with other conditions such as autism, severe ADHD/DAMP and Tourette syndrome are blurred, with several symptoms overlapping.

Compared with classic autism, Asperger syndrome is a milder handicap with a better outcome. Early diagnosis and accurate information about this disability for the family, teachers and others concerned should be at the heart of all intervention programmes.

Further reading

*Attwood, T. (1998) *Asperger's syndrome: a guide for parents and professionals.* London: Jessica Kingsley Publishers.

*Deudney, C. (2004) *Mental health in people with autism and Asperger syndrome: a guide for health professionals.* London: The National Autistic Society.

Frith, U. (ed.) (1991) *Autism and Asperger syndrome.* Cambridge: Cambridge University Press.

*Gerland, G. (1997) *A real person: life on the outside.* London: Souvenir Press.

*Gillberg, C. (2002) *A guide to Asperger syndrome.* Cambridge: Cambridge University Press.

*Jackson, L. (2002) *Freaks, geeks and Asperger syndrome: a user guide to adolescence.* London: Jessica Kingsley Publishers.

*Leicester City Council and Leicestershire County Council (1998) *Asperger syndrome – practical strategies for the classroom. A teacher's guide.* London: The National Autistic Society.

*NAS Autism Helpline (1999) *What is Asperger syndrome and how will it affect me? A guide for young people.* London: The National Autistic Society.

Ryan, R.M. (1992) Treatment-resistant chronic mental illness: is it Asperger's syndrome? *Hospital and Community Psychiatry* 43 (8), 807–811.

Sacks, O. (1993) A neurologist's notebook: an anthropologist on Mars. *The New Yorker* 69 (44), 106–125.

*Tantam, D. and Prestwood, S. (1999) *A mind of one's own: a guide to the special difficulties and needs of the more able person with autism or Asperger syndrome.* London: The National Autistic Society.

*Wing, L. (1996) *The autistic spectrum: a guide for parents and professionals.* London: Constable and Robinson.

*These titles are available from NAS Publications.
Tel: 020 7903 3595
Email: publications@nas.org.uk
Website: www.autism.org.uk/pubs

References

American Psychiatric Association (1994) *Diagnostic and statistical manual of mental disorders*, 4th edn (DSM-IV). Washington DC: APA.

Asperger, H. (1944) Die 'autistischen Psychopathen' im Kindesalter. *Archiv für Psychiatrie und Nervenkrankheiten* 117, 76–136. In German.

**Dewey, M. and Everard, M. (1974) The near-normal autistic adolescent. *Journal of Autism and Childhood Schizophrenia* 4, 348–356.

Ehlers, S. and Gillberg, C. (1993) The epidemiology of Asperger syndrome. A total population study. *Journal of Child Psychology and Psychiatry* 34, 1327–1350.

Gillberg, I.C. and Gillberg, C. (1989) Asperger syndrome – some epidemiological considerations: a research note. *Journal of Child Psychology and Psychiatry* 30 (4), 631–638.

Gillberg, C. (1991) Clinical and neurobiological aspects of Asperger syndrome in six family studies. In Frith, U. (ed.) *Autism and Asperger syndrome* (pp. 122–146). Cambridge: Cambridge University Press.

Gillberg, C. and Råstam, M. (1992) Do some cases of anorexia nervosa reflect underlying autistic-like conditions? *Behavioural Neurology* 5, 27–32.

Robinson, J.F. and Vitale, L.J. (1953) Children with circumscribed interest patterns. *American Journal of Orthopsychiatry* 24, 755–766.

Szatmari, P.A., Bremner, R. and Nagy, J. (1989) Asperger's syndrome: a review of clinical features. *Canadian Journal of Psychiatry* 34, 554–560.

Szatmari, P.A. (1991) Asperger's syndrome: diagnosis, treatment and outcome. *Psychiatric Clinics of North America* 14, 81–93.

**Wing, L. (1981) Asperger's syndrome: a clinical account. *Psychological Medicine* 11, 115–129.

World Health Organization (1993) *The ICD-10 classification of mental and behavioural disorders: diagnostic criteria for research.* Geneva: WHO.

**Copies of these articles are available from the NAS Information Centre. Tel: 0845 070 4004 Email: info@nas.org.uk

Appendix

Diagnostic criteria for obsessive-compulsive personality disorder (according to DSM-IV)

A pervasive pattern of preoccupation with orderliness, perfectionism, and mental and interpersonal control, at the expense of flexibility, openness, and efficiency, beginning by early adulthood and present in a variety of contexts, as indicated by four (or more) of the following:

(1) is preoccupied with details, rules, lists, order, organization, or schedules to the extent that the major point of the activity is lost

(2) shows perfectionism that interferes with task completion (e.g., is unable to complete a project because his or her own overly strict standards are not met)

(3) is excessively devoted to work and productivity to the exclusion of leisure activities and friendships (not accounted for by obvious economic necessity)

(4) is overconscientious, scrupulous, and inflexible about matters of morality, ethics, or values (not accounted for by cultural or religious identification)

(5) is unable to discard worn-out or worthless objects even when they have no sentimental value

(6) is reluctant to delegate tasks or to work with others unless they submit to exactly his or her way of doing things

(7) adopts a miserly spending style toward both self and others; money is viewed as something to be hoarded for future catastrophes

(8) shows rigidity and stubbornness.

Source: American Psychiatric Association (1994)

Notes